THE LAUGH-OUT-LOUD
CATS

in

# ONE MORE FOR THE ROAD

by

ADAM KOFORD

IF YOU EVER MEET ADAM KOFORD, MAKE HIM DRAW A PICTURE FOR YOU ON THIS PAGE.

FOR
MELVIN

SPECIAL THANKS TO ALL THOSE WHO'VE
READ, SHARED, AND SUPPORTED THESE
TWO FILTHY HOBO CATS OVER THE PAST
ELEVEN YEARS.

THIS MAP IZ JUST AS EFFECTIVE AT NITE AS IT IZ IN TEH DAY.
A. KOFORD

U'D THINK WITH ALL UR YEARS OF HOBO-ING, A BLIZZARD WOULDN'T CATCH US OFF GUARD — BUT HERE WE R!
A. KOFORD

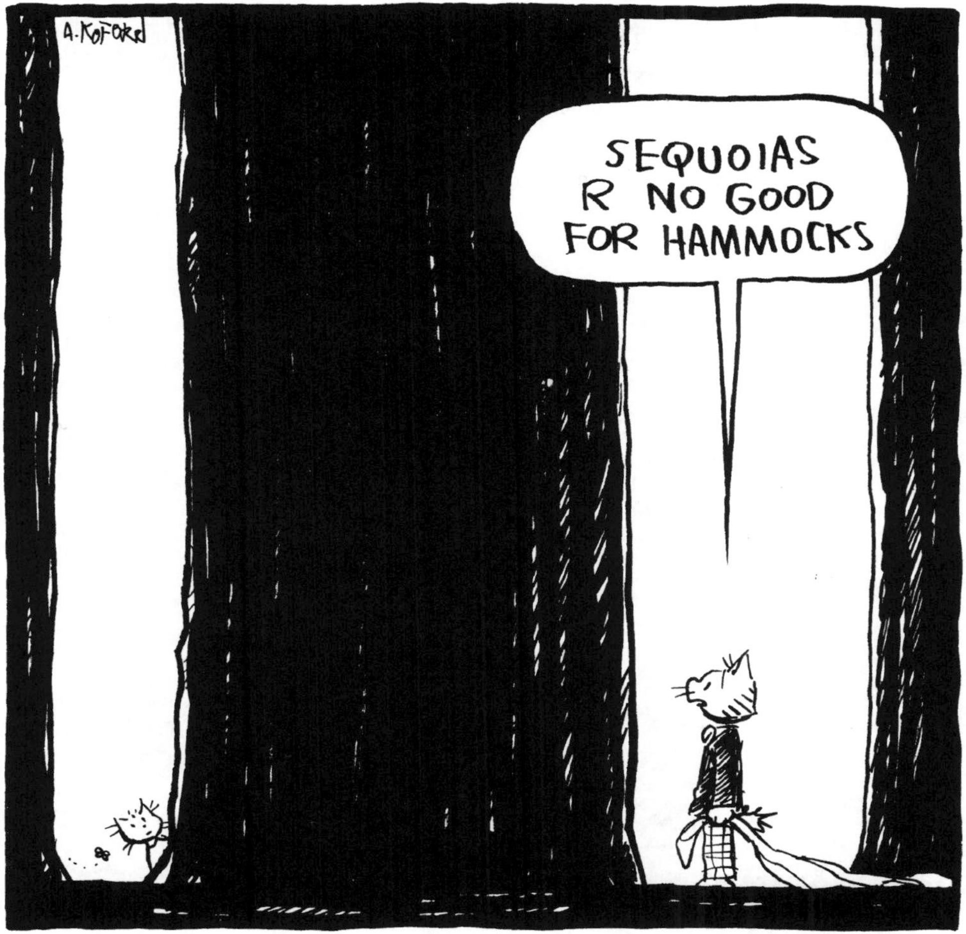
A. KOFORD
SEQUOIAS R NO GOOD FOR HAMMOCKS

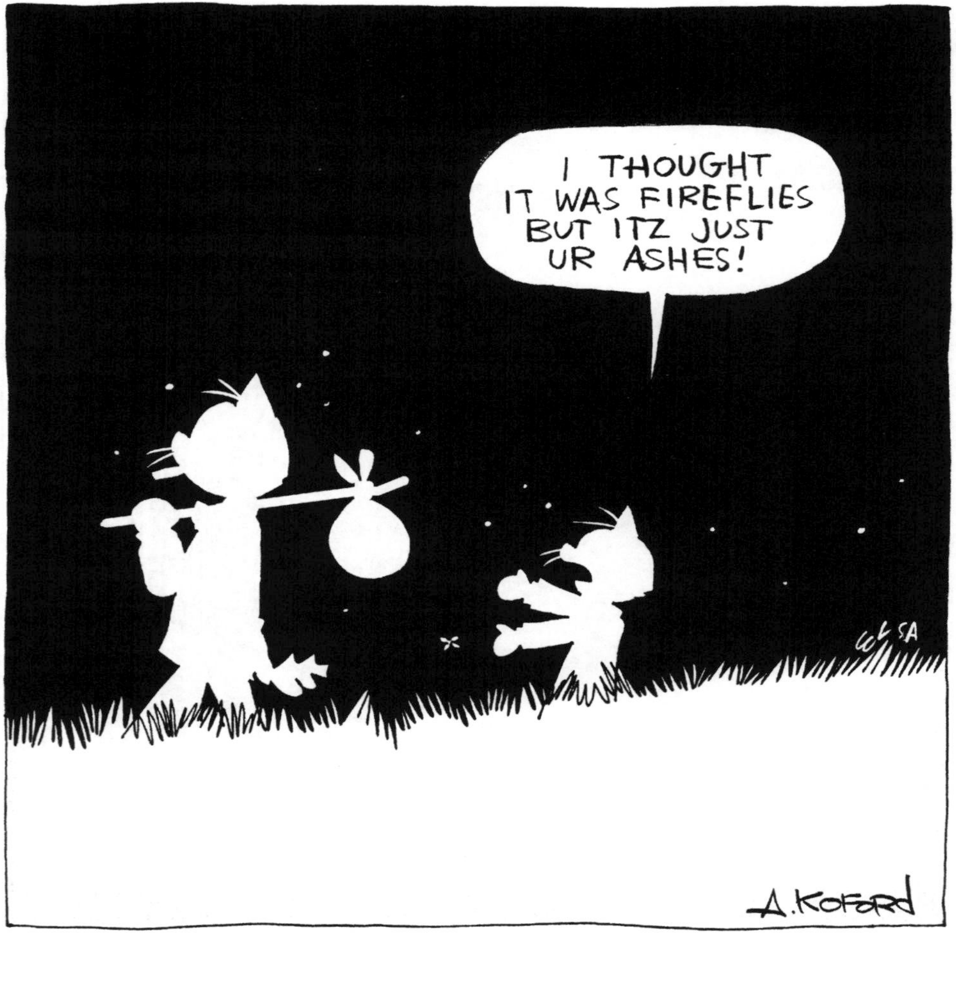
I THOUGHT IT WAS FIREFLIES BUT ITZ JUST UR ASHES!
A. KOFORD

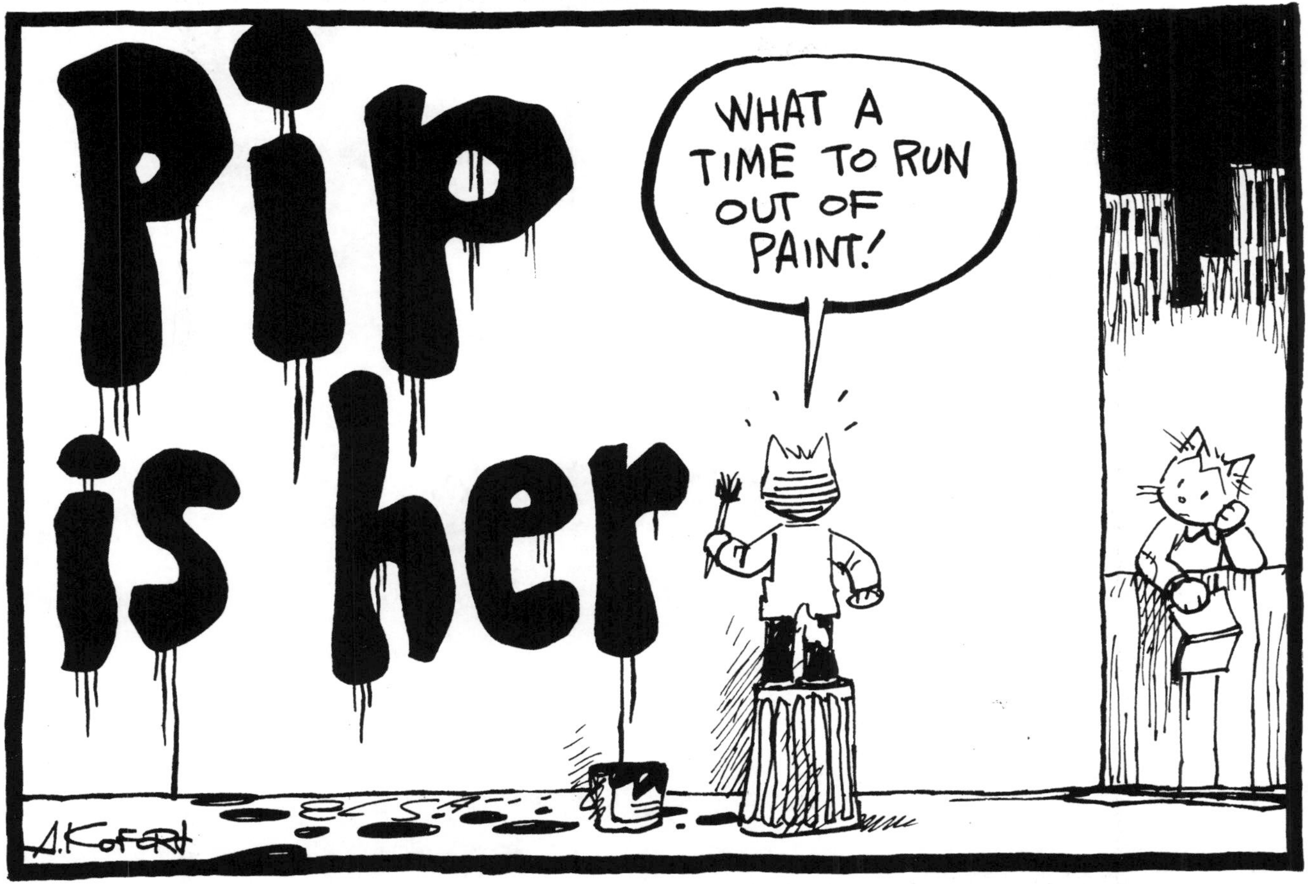
Pip is her
WHAT A TIME TO RUN OUT OF PAINT!
PAINT
A.KOFERT

I GUESS I WAITED TOO LONG TO WASH THESE CLOTHES—TEH MOLECULES R UNSTABLE.
A. KOFORD

UHH -- WHAT WAS I SAYING? I GUESS I KINDA DRIFTED OFF THERE FOR A SECOND...
A. KOFORD

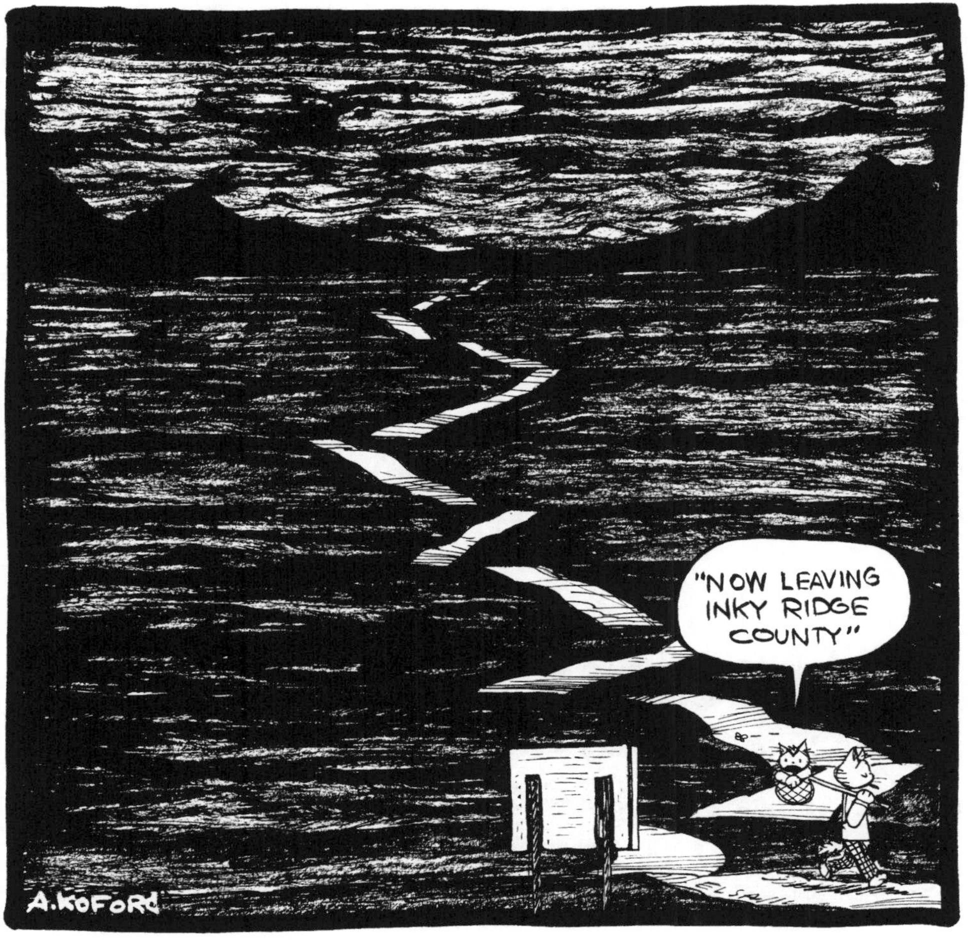
"NOW LEAVING INKY RIDGE COUNTY"
A.KOFORD

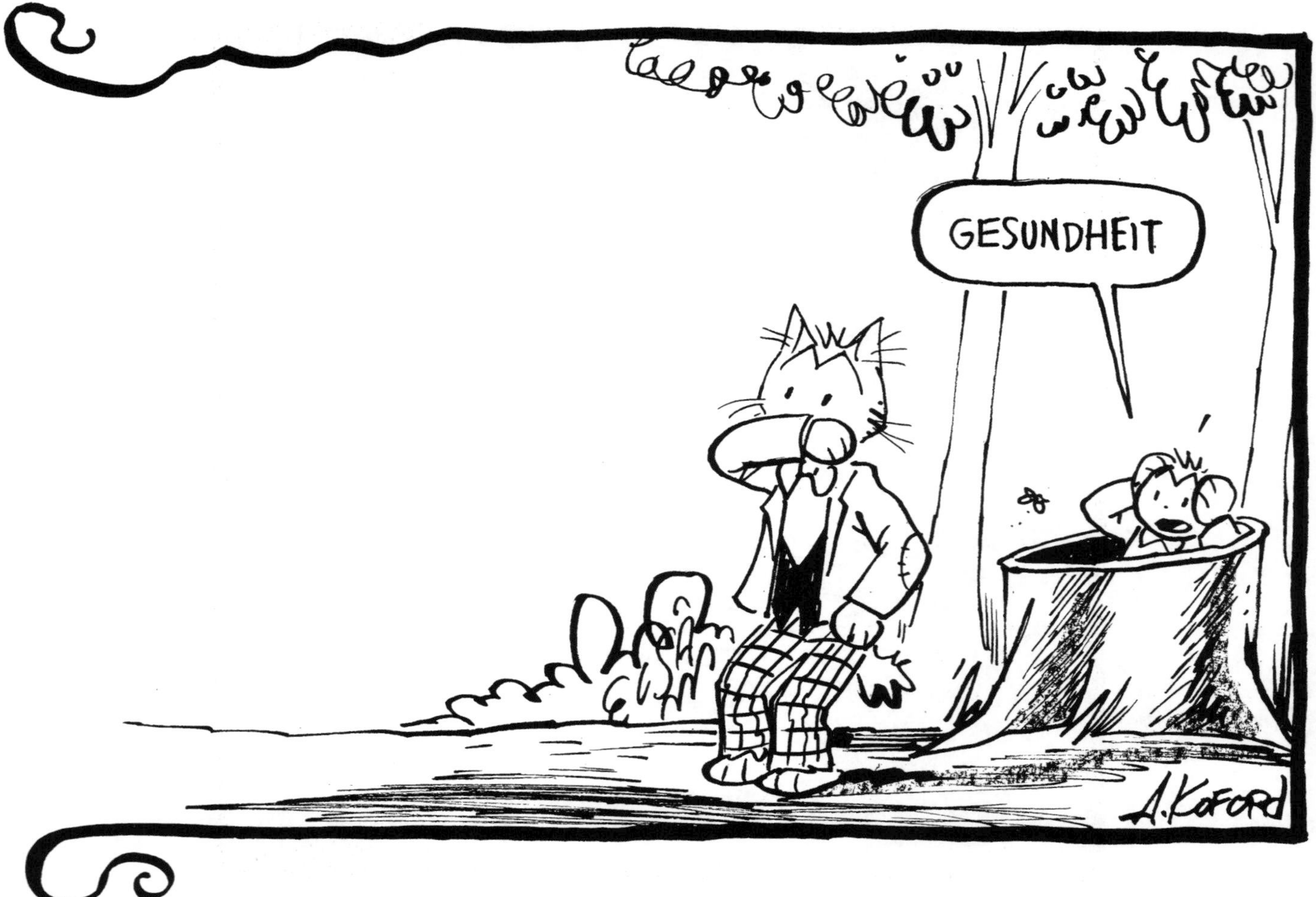
GESUNDHEIT
A. KOFORD

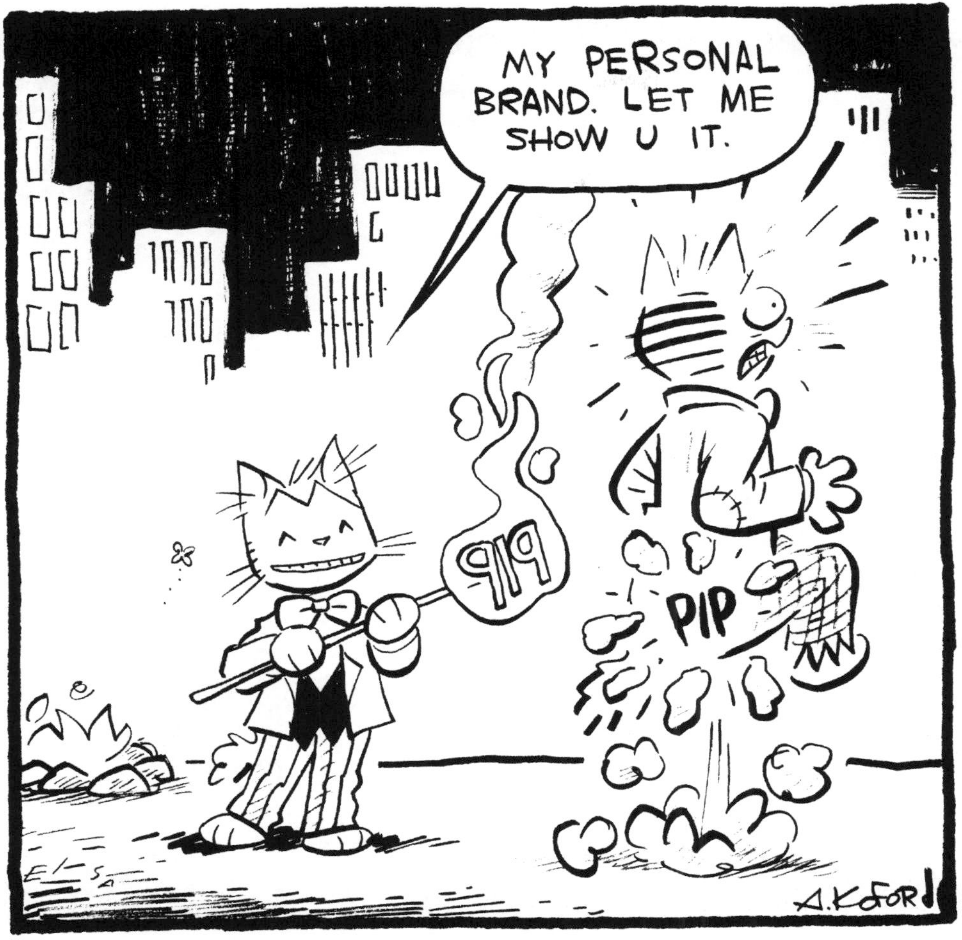
MY PERSONAL BRAND. LET ME SHOW U IT.
PIP
PIP
A. KOFORD

HOW COME UR A PUBLIC ENEMY BUT I'M JUST A PUBLIC NUISANCE?!
WANTED
A. KOFORD

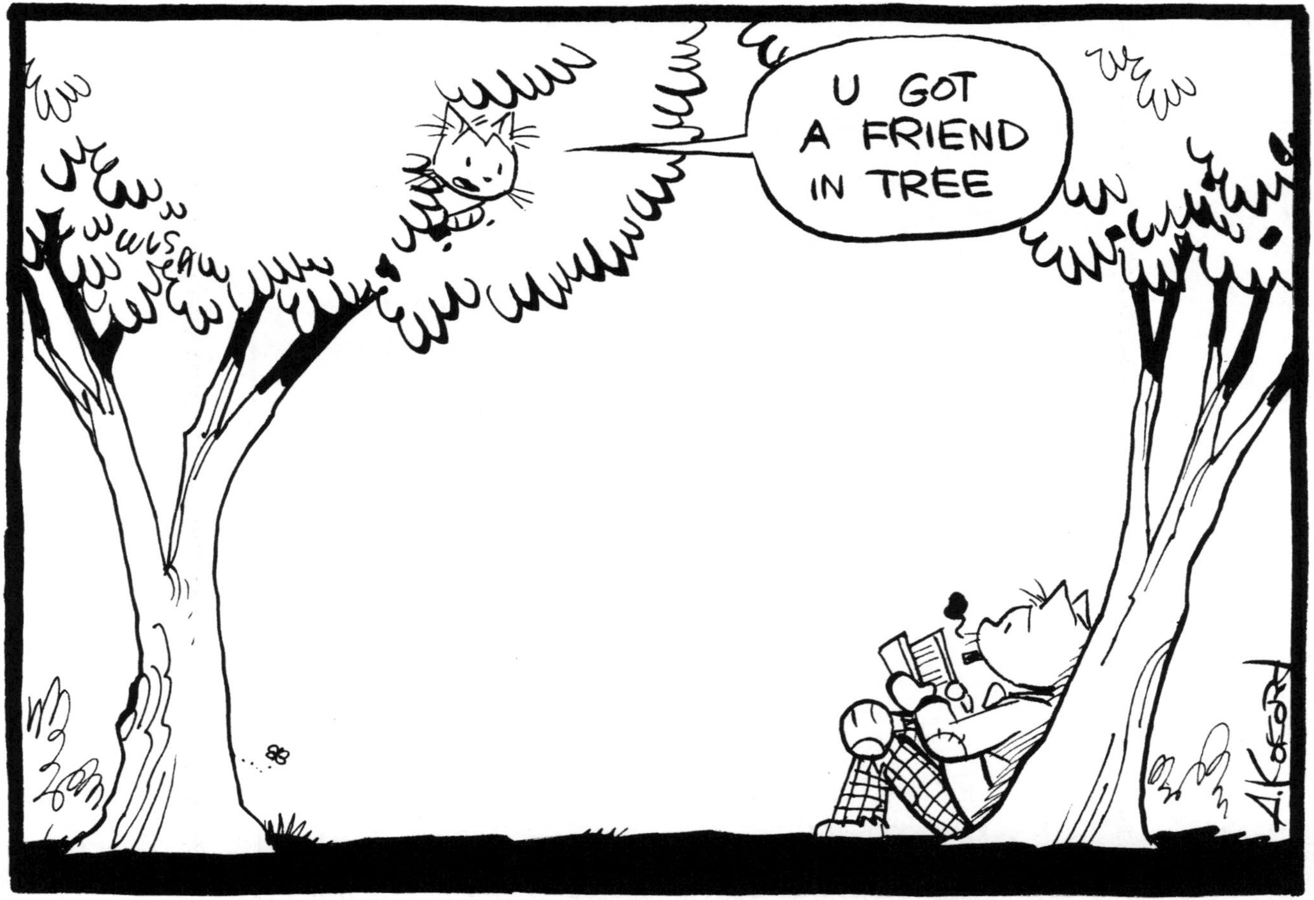
U GOT A FRIEND IN TREE

for Sale
Limited edition prints
I CALL 'EM LIMITED EDITION PRINTS CUZ I RAN OUT OF INK
A. KOFORD

U AIN'T NEVER HAD A FRIEND LIKE ME—OR ANY OTHER KIND EITHER.
A. KOFORD

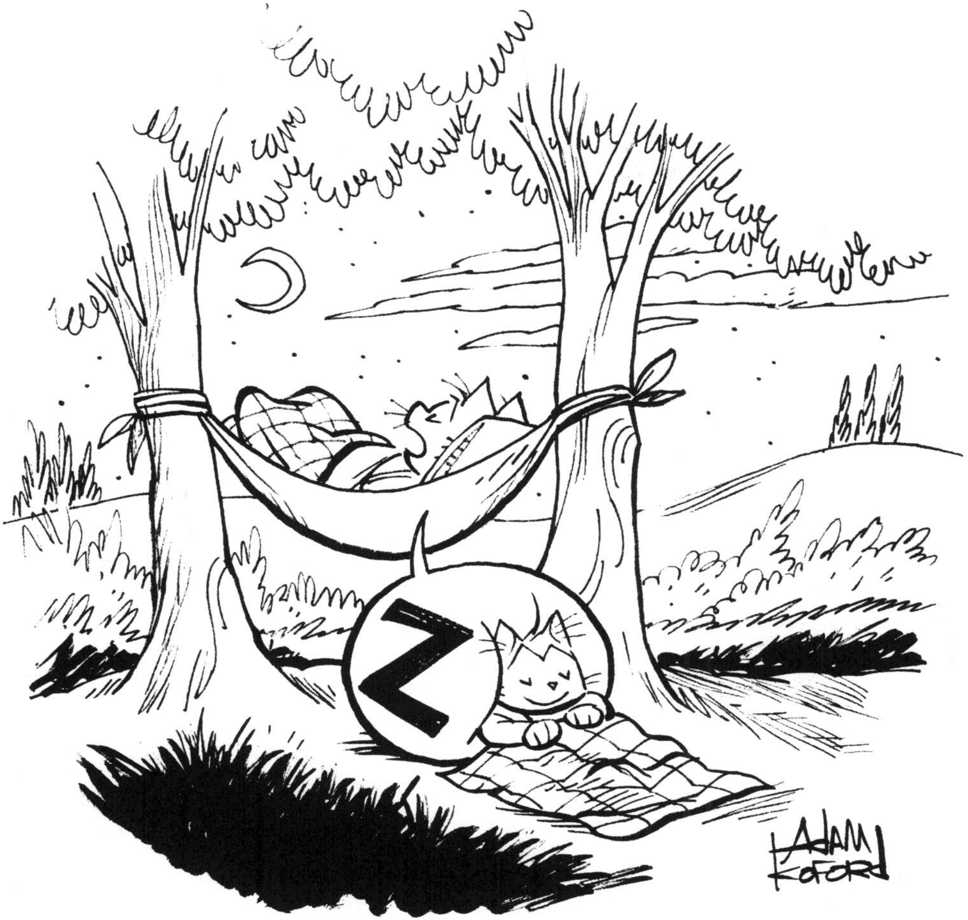
Z
ADAM KOFORD